CREATIVE COLOURING

CHRISTMAS
PATTERNS

Michael O'Mara Books Limited

This new edition first published in 2015
First published in Great Britain in 2014 by
Michael O'Mara Books Limited
9 Lion Yard
Tremadoc Road
London SW4 7NQ

A CIP catalogue record for this book is available from the British Library.

Papers used by Michael O'Mara Books Limited are natural, recyclable products
made from wood grown in sustainable forests. The manufacturing processes
conform to the environmental regulations of the country of origin.

ISBN: 978-1-78243-548-8

4 5 6 7 8 9 10

www.mombooks.com

Designed by Billy Waqar

Cover illustration by James Newman Gray

Illustrations by Sally Moret, Hannah Davies, Emily Parker, Jay Raine, Greg
Stevenson and Shutterstock.com

Printed and bound in China

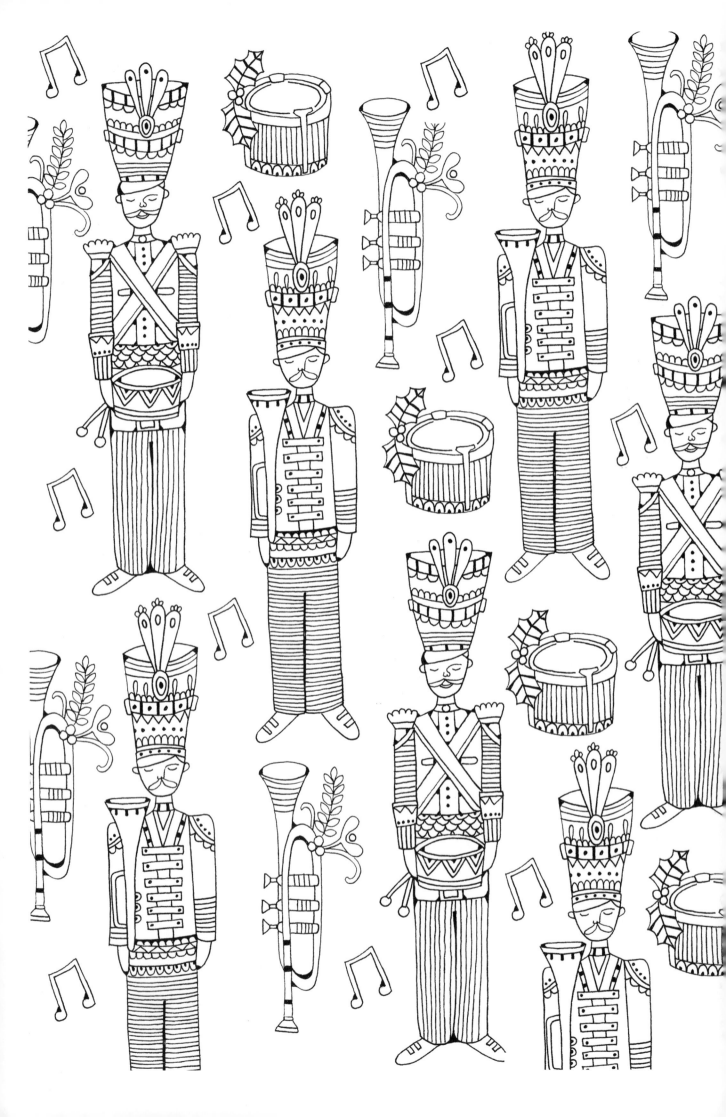

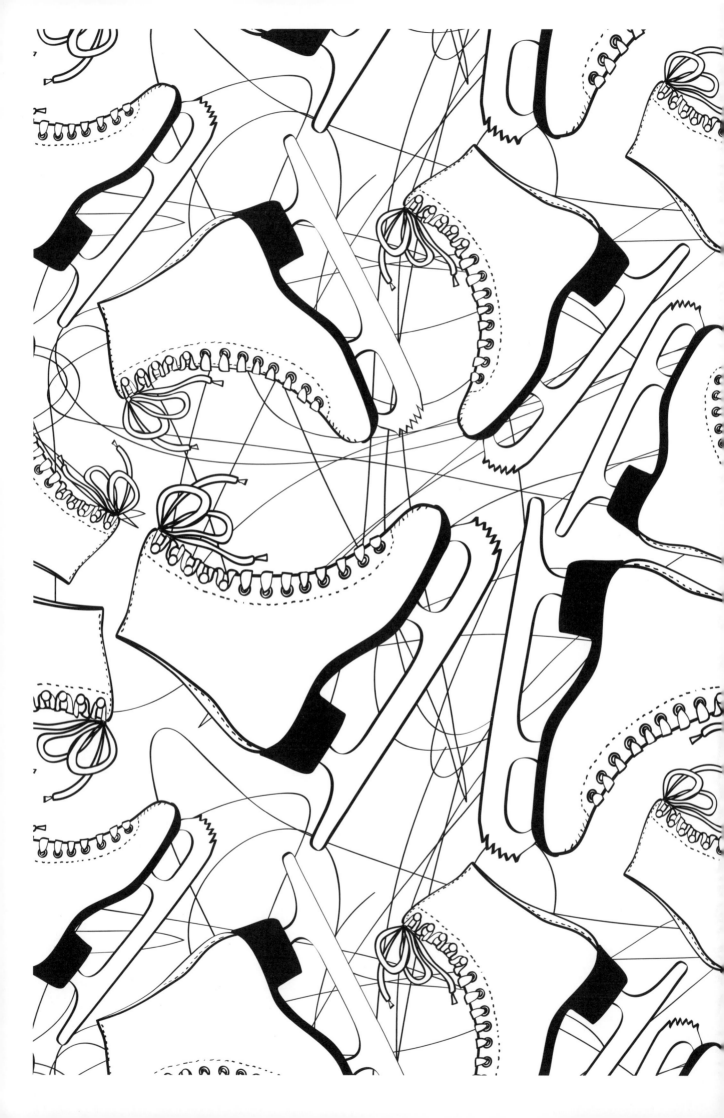

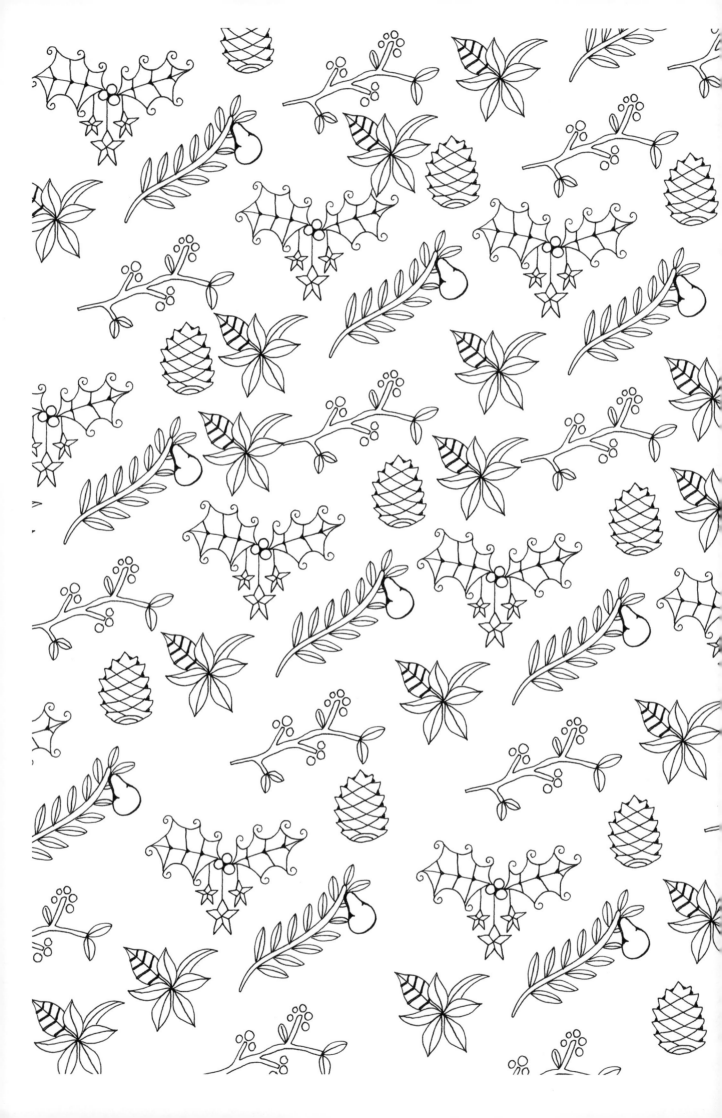

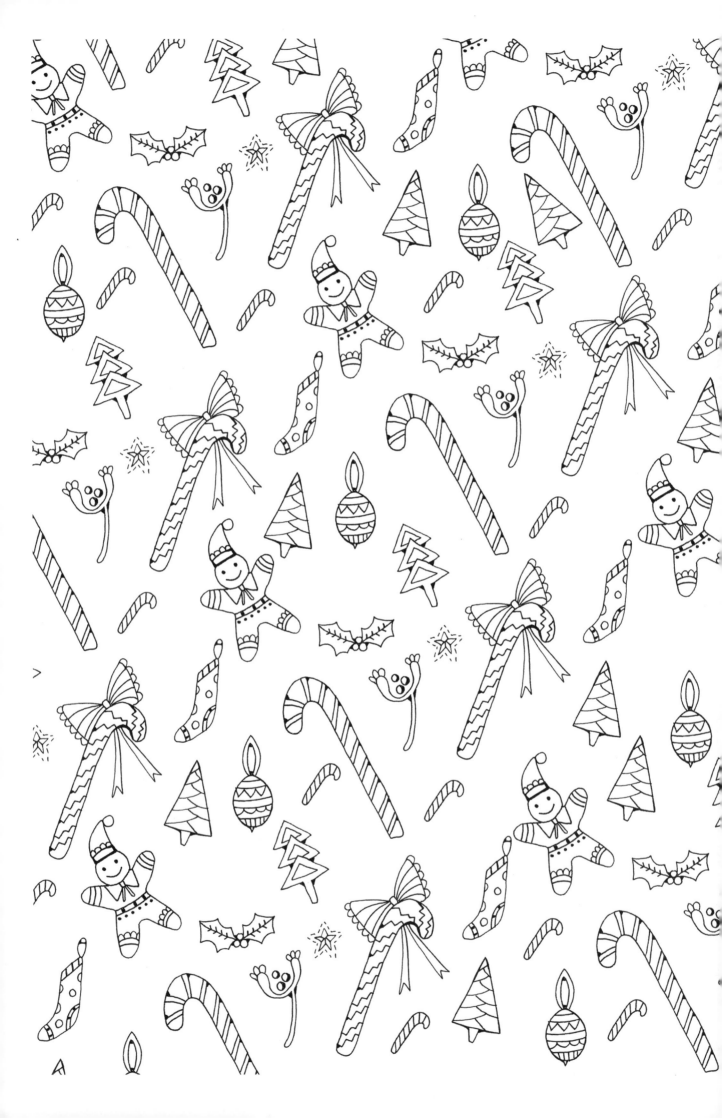

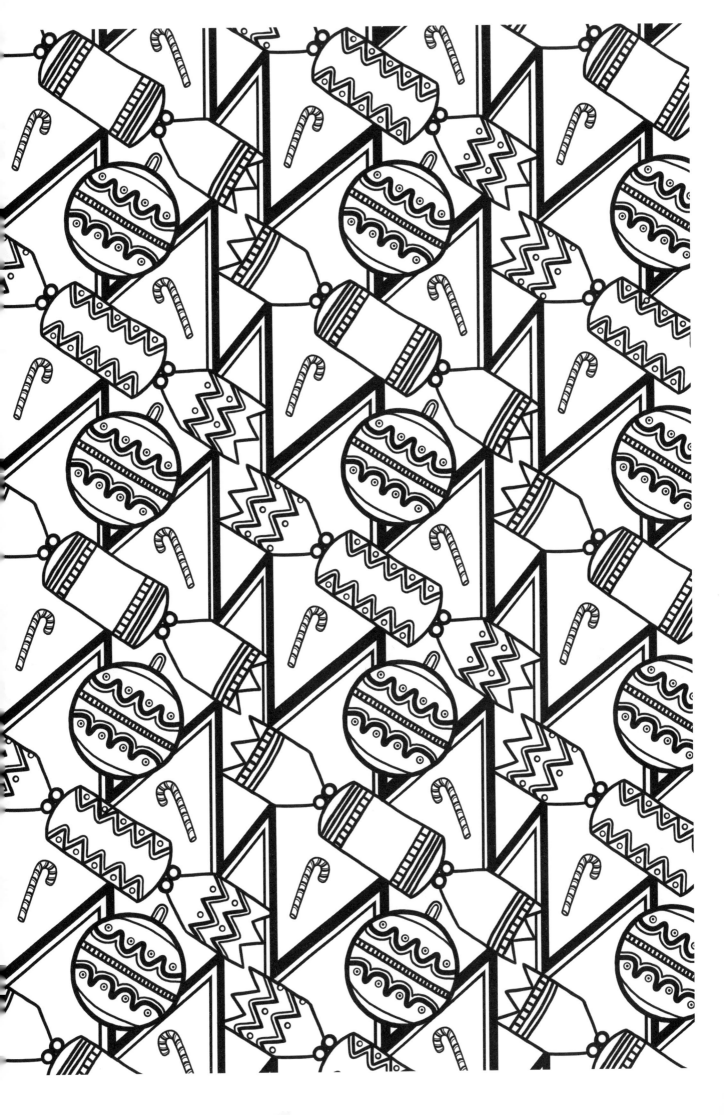

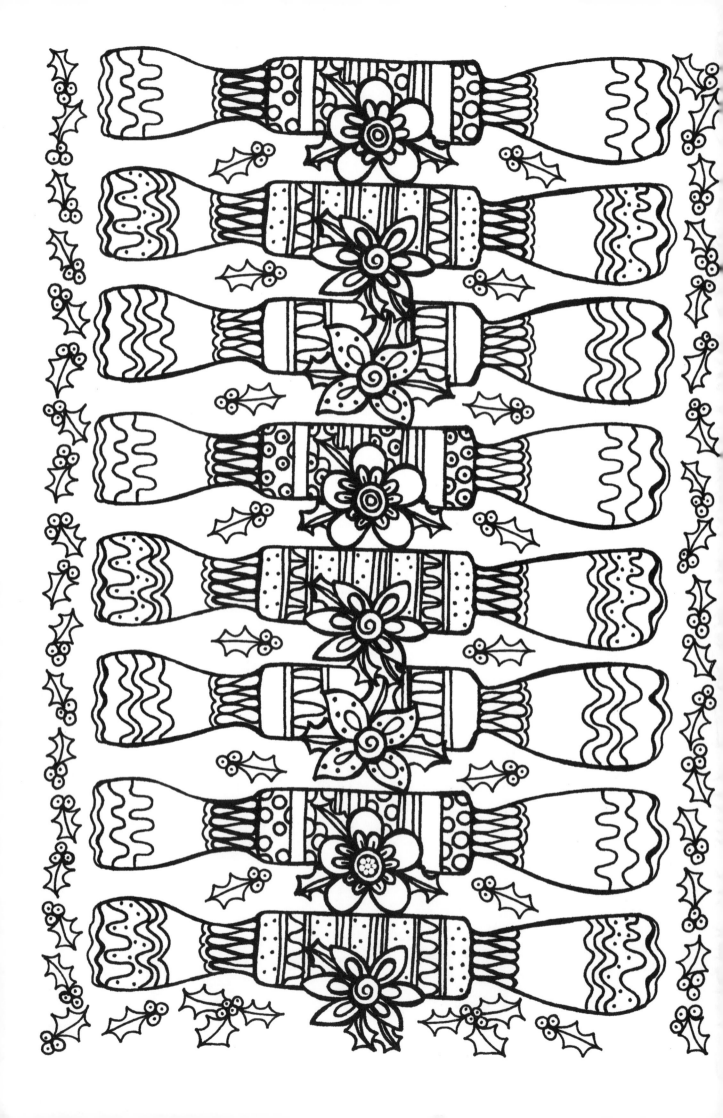